The adult' ____

This book is designed to h ____ eir
relationship with God.

It has three kinds of pages
1 Pages to fill in: pages tc ____selves, their
family and friends, God and people in the Bible who prayed.
2 'My choice' pages: these pages involve cutting an activity from
the back of the book and gluing it into place, then doing the activity.
Children can also use these pages for doing their own invented activities.
3 'Go and do it!': prayer activities to go off and do alone or with others.

You can use the book as part of a bedtime routine, weekly in a place and
time which suits you and your child, or as a dip-in book. The key thing is
that your child enjoys using the book and gets to know God better. So
feel free to adapt or miss out bits and to do the pages in the order which
works for you.

To make it easier and more fun for your child…
…get your child a nice pen, a glue stick and some scissors and attach
them to this book with a large rubber band. You could also get some
stickers and fun-shaped Post-it notes and put them in the pocket you are
about to make…

To make it easier for you…
…we've used a child-friendly version of the Bible (the CEV). We'd
recommend the Contemporary English Version or the Good News Bible,
or *The Big Bible Storybook* for younger children (aged 3 to 6 years). All of
these are available from all good Christian bookshops with the latter also
available direct from Scripture Union at www.scriptureunion.org.uk/shop
We've also labelled the back of each picture so when you've used some,
you can still tell which page they're from.

Now you've read this page…
…you need to turn over and use the instructions to turn this page into
a pocket. This will be useful when your child has cut out some of the
pictures or activities from the back and needs somewhere safe to put the
ones they want to save for later.

How to turn this page into a pocket

1 Cut along the thick lines.
2 Fold the paper back along the dotted lines.
3 Glue the folded sections onto the cover.

Alternatively...
...tear out this page and tape an A6 envelope onto the cover with the opening upwards.

When you have cut out some pictures and activities from the back of the book, put the ones you want to save for later in this pocket.

Glue here

Glue here

Glue here

My name is:

Write your name here!

and this is

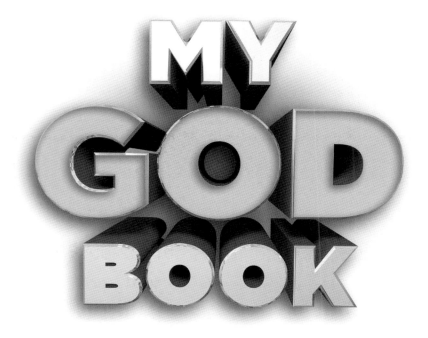

This is my special book
to help me be better
friends with God.

Copyright © Victoria Beech 2010
First published 2010, reprinted 2013
This edition first published 2016

ISBN 978 1 78506 406 7

Scripture Union, 207–209 Queensway, Bletchley,
Milton Keynes, MK2 2EB, England.
Email: info@scriptureunion.org.uk
Website: www.scriptureunion.org.uk

British Library Cataloguing-in-Publication Data.
A catalogue record of this book is available from the British Library.

Printed and bound in India by Thomson Press India Ltd

Cover design: Beatroot Media
Illustrations: Gill Chelski and Helen Jones

 Scripture Union is an international Christian charity working with churches
in more than 130 countries.

Thank you for purchasing this book. Any profits from this book support SU in
England and Wales to bring the good news of Jesus Christ to children, young
people and families and to enable them to meet God through the Bible and
prayer.

Find out more about our work and how you can get involved at:

www.scriptureunion.org.uk (England and Wales)
www.suscotland.org.uk (Scotland)
www.suni.co.uk (Northern Ireland)
www.scriptureunion.org (USA)
www.su.org.au (Australia)

Contents

Start here!

Write the date today here!

I started using this book on:

_____

You can use this book
every day
OR
every week
OR
whenever you like!
It's YOUR book.

☺ Some pages are for you to write or draw on.

☺ Go and do it! These pages have things for you to go and do.

☺ My choice! These pages have space for you to cut out and stick in an activity from the back of the book. (Don't forget to put the leftover ones in the pocket at the front.)

Have fun and enjoy your book with God.

Most of the Bible stories are in The Big Bible Storybook, a children's Bible available from Scripture Union. You can get it from your local Christian bookshop or www.scriptureunion.org.uk/shop

Me and God

If you could see God what would he look like?

Draw a picture of yourself and God here:

This is me
and God.

About God

God has lots of names in the Bible. Here are some:

Shepherd

Warrior

Judge   Yahweh

Lord   Provider

Underline God's names in this verse from the Bible.

"You are my mighty rock, my fortress, my protector, the rock where I am safe, my shield, my powerful weapon and my place of shelter." Psalm 18:2

How many are there?

What is your favourite name for God?

Use some of God's special names in a prayer to tell him he's great.

About me

God knows all about you and loves you very much!

Fill in the gaps about you.

I am _____ years old.

My favourite colour is _____.

I am _____ cm tall.

I love to _____.

My favourite game is _____.

I am glad God made me _____.
(for example, strong, fast, tall, kind, curly-haired)

About God

What do you think Jesus thought of children?

Read or ask someone to read to you from Mark 10:13–16. It's also on page 194 of The Big Bible Storybook.

Jesus loves everyone, including children! Draw a picture of you being welcomed by Jesus, like the children in the story. What do you want to say to Jesus? Write it under your picture!

What do you think the children might have chatted with Jesus about?

Imagine this: you and Jesus are having a chat. What might you talk about?

Me:

Jesus:

Have a chat with Jesus now! Find somewhere comfortable, sit down and close your eyes and imagine Jesus is with you giving you a hug – now chat with him.

You can chat out loud or in your head – Jesus can still hear! Remember to listen out for what Jesus might say to you!

My choice

Cut out and stick in an activity from the back of the book over these words. Or invent your own God-activity using one of the pictures, a Post-it note or something else to help you chat with God.

Go and do it!

Think of something you want to thank God for and draw or write it onto a balloon. Then put on some praise music and play hitting the balloon around the room.

You could do this with your family or some friends. Each write or draw something to thank God for on a balloon, then have fun bopping them to each other. Get one person to be the music master. When they stop the music, everyone should catch a balloon and thank God for the thing on it.

About Hannah praying 1

Read or ask someone to read to you part 1 of Hannah's story in the Bible in 1 Samuel 1:2–8. It's also on page 58 of The Big Bible Storybook.

Draw a circle round the right answer:

Hannah had no:

children

pigs

necklaces

washing

(Clue: look in verse 2.)

Hannah felt very:

happy

worried

excited

upset

(Clue: look in verse 6.)

What makes you upset?

Write or draw what makes you upset here:

Use this prayer to ask God to help you remember to talk with him next time you are upset:

> Dear God,
> Thank you that you listen to me when I am upset about something. Please help me to remember to talk with you next time I am upset.

Find out in part 2 what Hannah did when she was upset (to find out now go to page 18).

My choice

Cut out and stick in an activity from the back of the book over these words. Or invent your own God-activity using one of the pictures, a Post-it note or something else to help you chat with God.

Sorry, God

Choose a picture from picture page 2 of something you would like to say sorry to God for. Glue the picture on this page. If you can't find the right picture, draw your own. Draw a big cross through the picture and say to God, "I know this was wrong, God, and I'm sorry."

Remember that the Bible says God forgives everyone who's really sorry.

About Hannah praying 2

Look back at page 14 to remember part 1 of Hannah's story. Read or ask someone to read to you part 2 of Hannah's story in the Bible in 1 Samuel 1:9–18. It's also on page 58 of The Big Bible Storybook.

Draw a circle round the right answer:

When Hannah was upset she:

shouted   talked to God

hid

kicked something

(Clue: look in verse 9.)

Hannah was:

crying

dancing   shouting

singing

(Clue: look in verse 10.)

Hannah did different things to tell God how upset she was. She:

1 prayed out loud
2 cried
3 prayed silently in her head

Why not try out a new way of praying? You could do one of the above (don't pretend to cry though!), or try out one of these:

A smile prayer – smile while telling God silently about good things which make you smile.

A jumping prayer – jumping up and down to tell God about things which make you excited.

A kneeling prayer – kneeling to show God you are sorry for something you have done.

Find out in part 3 what God did for Hannah (to find out now go to page 28).

My choice

Cut out and stick in an activity
from the back of the book over
these words. Or invent your
own God-activity using one of
the pictures, a Post-it note or
something else to help you chat
with God.

Go and do it!

What toys do you like to play with?

Invent a way to use it/that/them to thank God for all the good things he does for you.

Here are some ideas:

1 Use Meccano or any building kits to create something and use it to praise God for creating everything!

2 Use play people or dolls to make a scene of something you like doing, such as going to the park.

3 Use play dough or paper and glue to make a model or collage of things you are thankful to God for.

You could take a picture of your invention and glue it in this book, or stick it on the fridge to remind you to thank God whenever you play with that toy.

About my family

Here is a picture of my family:

Draw or glue in a photo of your family.

Write everyone's name and draw a line from their name to their picture.

What do the people in your family like?

Draw or write one thing for each person. Then draw a line from it to them.

You might find some useful pictures at the back.

We all like different things. God made us all different, and loves all of us.

Thank God for all the different things your family likes and for loving all of you.

About Bible families

There are lots of different families in the Bible.

Can you match up each person with their family?
(You can look up the answers in the Bible.)

Jacob (a twin)
Genesis 25:22–26

Miriam (older sister)
Exodus 2:1–4

Joseph (had three
step-mums!)
Genesis 35:23–26

Esther (adopted)
Esther 2:7

Sometimes the brothers and sisters in the Bible helped each other.

Which of the children in the pictures helped rescue her baby brother from being killed? Exodus 2:5–10

Sometimes the brothers and sisters in the Bible had fights.

Which of the children in the pictures was a show-off and got put down a well by his brothers? Genesis 37:12–23

But God still loved them and helped them to be friends again.

Say sorry to God for something wrong you have done to a brother or sister or friend. (You might find a useful picture to stick in here at the back.)

Plan to do something to help them and show them God's love.

My choice

Cut out and stick in an activity from the back of the book over these words. Or invent your own God-activity using one of the pictures, a Post-it note or something else to help you chat with God.

Ask God

Draw or glue a picture from the back here of something good you find difficult to do. Ask God to help you and then draw God helping you.

About Hannah praying 3

Look back at pages 14 and 18 to remember parts 1 and 2 of Hannah's story.

Read or have someone read to you part 3 of Hannah's story in the Bible in 1 Samuel 1:19–20; 2:1. It's also on page 58 of The Big Bible Storybook.

Draw a circle round the right answer:

When Hannah went home she had a:

tantrum   baby boy

party

new kitten

(Clue: look in verse 20.)

When this happened Hannah:

felt happy   thanked God

laughed

(Clue: look in verse 1.)

God listened to Hannah's prayer and answered her.

When God did this, Hannah talked to God again, this time telling him how happy he had made her.

Think of something good God has done for you which you could thank him for and draw it here:

You could also sing a "thanks" song to God!

About my friends

Here are my friends:

Draw a picture of your friends or write their names here.

Thank God for each of your friends by name.

What would make a best friend?

Tick the boxes that describe a best friend!

☐ Generous

☐ Thinks you're great

☐ Always there

☐ Understands how you feel

☐ Helps you

God is the best friend ever! He could tick every box!

Thank God for being such a good friend!

You could add him to your picture on page 30.

My choice

Cut out and stick in an activity from the back of the book over these words. Or invent your own God-activity using one of the pictures, a Post-it note or something else to help you chat with God.

Go and do it!

Try out this special bedtime prayer. You can invent new bits for it too!

Roll down your covers to the end of your bed, then as you do this prayer, gradually roll the covers back up again.

1 Thank God for somewhere your feet have been today. (Roll the covers over your feet.)

2 Say sorry to God for something wrong you did today. (Roll the covers over your knees.)

3 Thank God for something you ate and is now in your tummy. (Roll the covers over your tummy.)

4 Ask God to help you sleep well and to help someone you know who needs his help with something. (Roll the covers over your shoulders.)

About my family

What are the best things about your family?

Draw them or write their names and the best thing about them on this and the next page.

There are some ideas down the side of this page.

Kind

Good cook

Generous

Loving

Patient

Good footballer

Funny

Helps me

Say a short prayer to thank God for the wonderful people in your family.

Now think of a way you can tell them how great they are. You could make them a card or write it on a balloon and give it to them. Or you could make up a poem or song about them.

See how many you can do this week!

My choice

Cut out and stick in an activity from the back of the book over these words. Or invent your own God-activity using one of the pictures, a Post-it note or something else to help you chat with God.

Ask God

Is there something you would like God's help with?

Draw a picture of what you would like God to do. You could use stickers or some of the pictures from the back to help you. As you work, ask God to help.

About me

What makes you happy?

How do you like to show people you are happy?

Tick the box or boxes, then draw a picture of you showing you're happy!

☐ Running very fast
☐ Skipping
☐ Shouting
☐ Singing
☐ Dancing
☐ Writing poems
☐ Smiling
☐ Jumping up and down
☐ Spinning like a top

☐ _____

Write your own one here!

You can use these ways to show God you are happy. They can all be types of prayer!

Look up these verses and draw a line to the type of prayer in the verse. Draw your own pictures to show what the people in the Bible did!

2 Samuel 6:14   Jumping

2 Chronicles 29:30   Shouting

Acts 3:8   Singing

Leviticus 9:24   Dancing

Practise your favourite action now, and use it to let God know next time you are happy about something.

About Miriam praying

There are lots of different ways to pray.

Read or ask someone to read to you Exodus 15:19–21 and see if you can spot how Miriam prays to God.

It's also on page 43 of The Big Bible Storybook and, although it doesn't mention Miriam by name, it does talk about what the people did.

Draw a picture or write what Miriam did to tell God how happy she was.

Miriam was happy because God had saved her and all the Israelite people from being slaves to the Egyptians.

What could you thank God for?

Sing a song to thank God.

Or use this one, adding in your own words:

Thank you God for _____!
Thank you God for _____!
Thank you God for _____!
You're so good to us.

Hallelujah, thank you God!
Hallelujah, thank you God!
Hallelujah, thank you God!
You're so good to us.

My choice

Cut out and stick in an activity
from the back of the book over
these words. Or invent your
own God-activity using one of
the pictures, a Post-it note or
something else to help you chat
with God.

About God

The Bible says:

"Before I even speak a word, you know what I will say." Psalm 139:4

Who do you think "you" is?

God knows what we are thinking, so we don't need to pretend to him.

When we talk with God, we can always tell him the truth about how we feel.

Draw a circle around the face which shows how you feel. Then talk to God about why you feel like that. God is listening!

About my friends

Have you ever done something wrong to one of your friends?

Draw or write it here, or find a picture from the back of the book and glue it in.

How did your friend feel? Circle the right face!

God felt like that too, because he loves your friend and is sad when they are sad.

Did you say sorry to your friend and to God?

The Bible calls things we do wrong "sins". What do you think God does when we are sorry for our sins?

Look it up in Psalm 103:3.

When we say sorry to God and really mean it, he forgives us, and we can start again.

Look at Psalm 103:12 to find out how far away God puts our sins.

Why not say sorry to God now? He is listening.

Want to hear more about it? Get hold of a book called The Purple Balloon (£4.99, 978 1 84427 265 5) and see what Xanthe finds out about God forgiving us!

Ask God

Do you know people who need help? Write or draw them here, or find a picture in the back of the book and stick it in. Next to them, write or draw the kind of help they need. Then ask God to get them that help.

My choice

Cut out and stick in an activity from the back of the book over these words. Or invent your own God-activity using one of the pictures, a Post-it note or something else to help you chat with God.

About me

What's your favourite dinner? Draw it here:

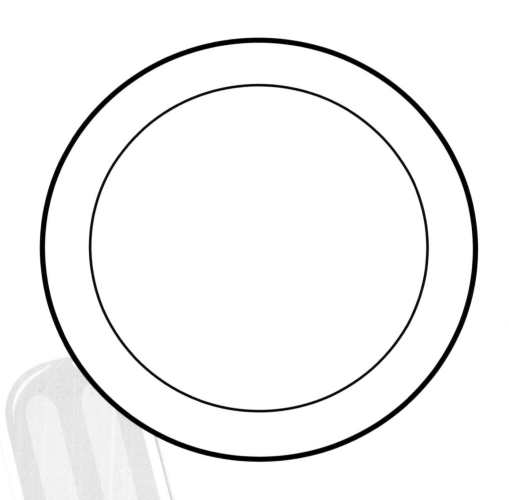

Now thank God for it!

About my family

Find the pictures which show somewhere someone in your family went today and add a tiny picture of them to that picture. If some places are missing, you could draw them too!

Thank God for keeping you all safe.

About me

My favourite way to go places is:

Colour in your favourite, or add it in the space.

Finish this short "thank you" poem, then say it to God:

Dear God, as you know,

My favourite way to go,

Is _____.

Thank you for this way to go,

Now I've finished, off I go!

(Zoom round the room acting out your favourite way to "go"!)

If you enjoyed this, you may like the song "I'm gonna click, click, click" (number 150 in the kidsource songbook).

Draw yourself in your favourite way to go!

My choice

Cut out and stick in an activity from the back of the book over these words. Or invent your own God-activity using one of the pictures, a Post-it note or something else to help you chat with God.

Praise God

Invent some new words to describe God by putting together some of the bits of words on this page. Use your new words in a prayer telling God how great he is.

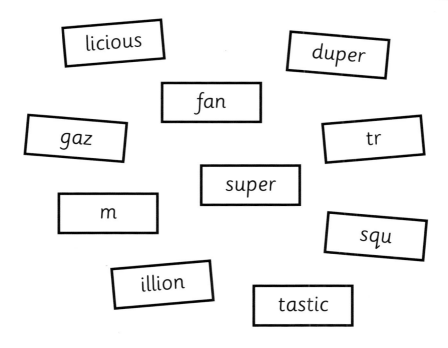

licious

duper

fan

gaz

tr

super

m

squ

illion

tastic

Keep asking

When you ask for something, do you keep on asking until you get it? Do you think God is happy for you to keep on asking him for things?

Read about a lady who did just this in Luke 18:1–8.

What did the lady in the story keep doing?

a) sulking
b) skipping
c) asking for help

Why did Jesus tell this story? (There's a clue in verse 1.)

Is there something you have asked God for which he hasn't done yet?

Are there things which you would like to ask God to do?

Maybe there are some people you would like to pray for.

Draw them or write their names here and write a note to remind you and God what you would like him to do.

Write today's date, and come back to this page in a little while to pray for them again and see what God has done. When you pray for them again, you could add that date too!

Go and do it!

Invent a way to remind you to keep asking like the lady in the story.

Decorate the wristband at the edge of this page, then cut down the dotted line. Glue the wristband round your wrist to remind you to pray! PUSH stands for:

Pray Until Something Happens

You could put a note by your bed to remind you to ask God each night before you sleep.

And remember: the Bible says God is NOT like the judge in the story, and he loves his people and will "hurry and help them" (verse 8).

Glue here

My choice

Cut out and stick in an activity from the back of the book over these words. Or invent your own God-activity using one of the pictures, a Post-it note or something else to help you chat with God.

About me

Fill in the gaps about you.

My class is _____.

My teacher is _____.

My school is _____.

Draw yourself at school:

My favourite lesson is _____

because _____

_____

_____.

Thank God for all the things you have written about. You could put them into this song and sing it to God:

Thank you God for _____!
Thank you God for _____!
Thank you God for _____!
You're so good to us.

Hallelujah, thank you God!
Hallelujah, thank you God!
Hallelujah, thank you God!
You're so good to us.

Repeat the verse adding in your class, teacher and favourite lesson.

You could sing this song on your way to school!

Jesus talks about praying 1

Read or ask someone to read to you Luke 18:9–14, then draw a picture of the two men praying. You'll find this story on page 153 of The Big Bible Storybook.

The Big Bible Storybook calls them Mr Proud and Mr Sorry.

Which man do you think Jesus wants us to be like?

Sorry, God

Cut out the pictures of the thought bubble, the speech bubble and the hands from the back of the book and glue them on this page.

☺ Draw or write in the thought bubble something you want to say sorry to God for thinking.
☺ Draw or write in the speech bubble something you want to say sorry to God for saying.
☺ Draw or write in the hands something you want to say sorry to God for doing.

Something amazing you should know: God forgives you!

About my friends

Do any of your friends need you to pray for them? Maybe they are ill or are having problems with something.

Draw them or write their names here. Say a prayer asking God to help them. Then draw a big heart around their name to show God's love is all around them.

Make sure you remember to keep praying for them. God likes us to keep asking him.

You could draw more hearts each time you pray.

My choice

Cut out and stick in an activity from the back of the book over these words. Or invent your own God-activity using one of the pictures, a Post-it note or something else to help you chat with God.

Jesus talks about praying 2

Jesus' friends once asked Jesus how to pray. Do you know what he told them?

You can look it up in Luke 11:1–4. It's also on page 179 of The Big Bible Storybook.

Write or draw a picture of your favourite bit here:

Try out using this prayer when you talk with God, or try this version. (You can sing it to the tune of "Hallelujah (Your love is amazing)" by Brenton Brown.) Draw pictures around these words which show how amazing God is, the food that you eat, some of the wrong things you've done and some examples of how God wants us to live.

Father, you're amazing.
Please do things here your way.
Please give us the food we
Need to live today.
Forgive us for wrong things.
Help us forgive others.
Show us how to live and
Keep us safe from harm.

Go and do it!

Some people find it helps them to pray in a certain place or use a special thing when they pray.

Here's how to make your own prayer hat:

1 Cut a strip of card about 5 cm wide and long enough to go around your head. Stick the ends together with sticky tape.

2 Cut strips of paper the same width and stick each end of them to opposite sides of the headband. Go all the way round the band so that the strips make the top of the hat.

3 Decorate your hat with things you like, such as feathers, glitter, tissue or raw pasta!

4 Wear your hat when you talk to God.

You could even make your own prayer den, a special place where you can go and talk with God. Build it using blankets, cushions, large cardboard boxes or a sheet.

My choice

Cut out and stick in an activity from the back of the book over these words. Or invent your own God-activity using one of the pictures, a Post-it note or something else to help you chat with God.

Praise God

Choose one of these words and write it in the space... or put one of your own!

always there

powerful

amazing

brilliant

the best

Lord

kind

caring

trustworthy

good

true

God, I think you are

_____

Make the page look amazing like God is.

You could read the page out loud to God. He likes to hear you talk to him.

Thank God

Draw some pictures of things you would like to thank God for. You could use pictures from the back of the book.

Write one word next to each picture to tell God what you like about it (for example "tasty" or "fun").

About Daniel praying 1

Read the story (or ask someone to read it to you) from Daniel 6:1–10. It's also on pages 99–104 in The Big Bible Storybook.

How often did Daniel pray?
a) every day
b) twice a day
c) three times a day

What did Daniel do when he prayed?
a) closed his eyes
b) put his hands together
c) knelt at a window

How often do you pray? Have you started praying more with My God Book?

Write or draw your favourite way to pray.

Daniel was a long way from his home in Jerusalem and the temple where he used to worship God. He used to pray looking out of the window, in the direction of Jerusalem.

Sometimes when we are not at home it's hard to remember to pray to God.

Draw here what you can see out of your window, then try out kneeling at a window to pray like Daniel.

If you are not at home, you could even use a compass to work out which way "home" is!

Praise God

Circle your favourite word to describe God in this verse from the Bible:

"But you, the Lord God, are kind and merciful. You don't easily get angry, and your love can always be trusted."

Psalm 86:15

Use the word you circled in a sentence prayer to God. Write it here:

My choice

Cut out and stick in an activity from the back of the book over these words. Or invent your own God-activity using one of the pictures, a Post-it note or something else to help you chat with God.

About Daniel praying 2

Read the story in Daniel 6:11–28. It's also on pages 99–104 in The Big Bible Storybook.

What happened to Daniel because he prayed?
a) Everyone liked him.
b) He visited the zoo.
c) He was put in a pit of lions.

What happened to Daniel because he prayed?
a) The lions ate him.
b) His friends rescued him.
c) God rescued him.

Sometimes people might not like us because we pray to God. But we can still pray to God.

Does anyone you know think it's silly to pray? Say a prayer for them now asking God to show them he is real like he showed the king.

You could draw a picture of them here with a love heart from God to them.

Go and do it!

Do a swinging prayer!

Swing on a swing in your garden or a park and think of lots of words to describe God. Here are some to start you off. Write some more here too!

wonderful

always loving

amazing

beautiful

never-ending

mighty

true

When you are going high enough, each time you go forwards call out one of your God-words as praise to God.

If you do this with someone pushing the swing, take it in turns with them — they should call out one when they push, then you call out one as you swing!

Praise God

Fill in the blanks to write your own prayer, then read it out loud to God.

God, you are _____.

I like the way you _____.

I am so glad you invented

_____

_____

_____

_____

_____

_____

_____

My choice

Cut out and stick in an activity from the back of the book over these words. Or invent your own God-activity using one of the pictures, a Post-it note or something else to help you chat with God.

Thank God

Inside each letter of the words "thank you", draw something you'd like to thank God for.

You might like to do some now and some more another day. See if you can remember all these things without looking at the page!

Praise God

God is so amazing, he is more than our minds can even imagine. The Bible often uses pictures to help describe what God is like.

Can you spot what these verses say God is a bit like? Match the verse with the right picture!

"The LORD is a mighty tower where his people can run for safety." Proverbs 18:10

"No other god is like you. We're safer with you than on a high mountain." 1 Samuel 2:2

"Sing joyful songs to the LORD! Praise the mighty rock where we are safe." Psalm 95:1

"Jesus replied: 'I am the bread that gives life! No one who comes to me will ever be hungry. No one who has faith in me will ever be thirsty.'" John 6:35

Think of your own way to describe God using things around you. You can fill in the blanks and even draw little pictures of the things God is a bit like round the edge.

God, you are a bit like

_____

because you

_____

_____

_____

God, you are a bit like

_____

because you

_____

_____

_____

God, you are a bit like

_____

because you

_____

_____

_____

Go and do it!

Try this "fingers and toes" prayer:

1 Touch each of the fingers on your left hand. As you touch each one, thank God for someone you love and something you love about them.

2 Touch each of the fingers on your right hand, thanking God for things you like to do.

3 Touch each of the toes on your left foot, thanking God for something he made.

4 Touch each of the toes on your right foot, asking God to be with each of the people you love, to help and take care of them.

My choice

Cut out and stick in an activity
from the back of the book over
these words. Or invent your
own God-activity using one of
the pictures, a Post-it note or
something else to help you chat
with God.

About Elijah praying 1

Elijah used to talk with God, and God would talk with him.

Read or ask someone to read to you what God told Elijah one day in 1 Kings 17:8–16. (Read it on page 77 of The Big Bible Storybook.)

Write or draw your answers to these questions.

What did Elijah ask the lady for?

What happened to the flour and oil?

Have you ever thought God might talk to you? What might he say?

Write, draw or stick in pictures or Post-its to show what God might be saying to you.

Did God do what he said he would do?

Yes or No?

We can trust God as what he says is true and will happen.

Spend a minute talking with God now, then spend a minute listening. Chat with someone about what you think God might have said to you.

Go and do it!

Pray and make your own flat bread!

As you knead it, ask God to feed all the people who do not have enough food. Write or draw your prayers here.

As you eat it, thank God for it and all the food you have to eat. Write or draw your prayers here.

How to make flat bread

You will need:
250 g plain white flour
250 g strong white bread flour
5 g quick-acting dried yeast
10 g salt
165 ml warm water
165 ml warmed natural yogurt
1 tbsp olive oil
A grown-up to help you!

Mix all the ingredients in a bowl (but not the grown-up; they won't taste very nice!).

Then knead the dough on a clean, floured work surface until smooth. As you do this, ask God to help everyone who does not have enough food.

Leave the dough in a warm place until it has doubled in size.

Tear off plum-sized pieces and use your hands to roll them into balls. Use a rolling pin to roll the balls into circles about 4 mm thick. Place on a board or tray, cover them with cling film and leave them for 30 minutes.

Get your grown-up to heat a frying pan until it is very hot. When the pan is ready, the grown-up should cook each circle of bread dough for one minute each side – watch the bread balloon! Repeat with all the dough. Alternatively, cook them for 1 to 2 minutes each side on a barbecue.

Remember to thank God as you eat!

Praise God

Read Psalm 150. How many instruments are used in the psalm to praise God?

Fill in the blanks below to create your own version with things you could use to praise God. If possible, get them all together and read your psalm while playing them! (You might need some friends to help you!)

Praise God with _____

and all kinds of _____.

Praise him with _____

and _____,

with _____

and _____.

Praise God with _____,

with clashing _____.

Let every living creature praise the Lord.
Shout praises to the Lord!

My choice

Cut out and stick in an activity from the back of the book over these words. Or invent your own God-activity using one of the pictures, a Post-it note or something else to help you chat with God.

About Elijah praying 2

Do you remember what God did for Elijah, the lady and her son?

Read or ask someone to read what happened next in 1 Kings 17:17–24.

Write or draw your answers to these questions. Or you could stick in a picture or use a Post-it!

What did Elijah do while he was praying?

What did God do to answer Elijah's prayer?

There are lots of ways to pray.

Sometimes it's good to touch someone who we are praying for, maybe by putting our hand on their hand or shoulder. But don't do anything that they won't be happy with.

If you know someone who is ill, why don't you go and pray with them? Maybe you could put your hand on theirs as you pray.

If you know people who are ill, write their names down here. Make sure you look out for God's answer to your prayer!

Ask God

Draw someone you would like God to do something for. Draw a big heart around them. Ask God to help them and show them his love.

Sorry, God

Find a picture from the back of the book of something you would like to say sorry to God for. Or write or draw your own.

When we are really sorry, God says, "I forgive you!"

My choice

Cut out and stick in an activity
from the back of the book over
these words. Or invent your
own God-activity using one of
the pictures, a Post-it note or
something else to help you chat
with God.

Praise God

What would you like to say to God?

Choose some of the words below to make a sentence to God.

wonderful   strong

            are

brilliant   God

            holy

                    you

    incredible

                cool

true

        I think

Jesus talks about praying 3

Jesus talked a lot about prayer! He does it again in Matthew 6:5–7.

Put a circle round the sorts of prayers you think Jesus likes:

Help!

I'M GREAT AT PRAYER!

Oh great and glorious God, efficacious in all your ways, triumvirate in nature!

Invent a prayer to God and write it here:

Remember, God wants you to talk to him as you; not copying someone else, or showing off. He wants to talk to YOU!

Go and do it!

Try out this "getting dressed" prayer. As you put on each piece of clothing, say one of these prayers:

Hat: Thank you, God, for my imagination and all the ideas I will have today.

Make up your own prayers for other things like scarves or coats.

T-shirt/top: Thank you, God, for my arms and all the things they will do today.

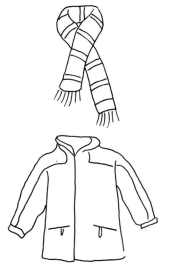

Shorts/trousers/skirt/dress: Thank you, God, for my legs and all the walking, jumping and skipping they will do today.

Socks/shoes: Thank you, God, for my feet and all the places they will take me today.

My choice

Cut out and stick in an activity from the back of the book over these words. Or invent your own God-activity using one of the pictures, a Post-it note or something else to help you chat with God.

About prayer

The Bible talks a lot about prayer. Read this verse to find out what the prayers of God's people (that includes you) are like.

"... the four living creatures and the twenty-four elders each ... had a harp and a gold bowl full of incense, which are the prayers of God's people." Revelation 5:8

What's your favourite smell? Write or draw it here!

Incense is something that smells very sweet when it's burnt.

Find something which makes a nice smell and use it while you say some prayers to God.

For example, you could cut or peel an orange, smell some herbs, or ask permission to borrow some perfume.

There is something else God does when we pray.

"And if we know that God listens when we pray, we are sure that our prayers have already been answered." 1 John 5:15

Go back through this book and find any prayers which God has answered.

When you find one, remember to thank God.

You could do this by writing or drawing a "thank you" prayer here or try one of the ideas on the next page.

Go and do it!

Invent a really fun way to thank God when he has answered one of your prayers.

You could make up a football-style chant to thank him. Here's one to get you started:

God! You are so great!
God! You are so great!
You heard me
when I prayed!

Write some more here!

Or you could sing a song to thank God. Choose your favourite praise song and sing it to him. He'll love it!

Or you could invent a "thank you" dance to some music you love and dance to thank God.

My choice

Cut out and stick in an activity
from the back of the book over
these words. Or invent your
own God-activity using one of
the pictures, a Post-it note or
something else to help you chat
with God.

About God

If you've got to this part of the book, you have been keeping God pretty busy.

What do you think God is doing while you're praying?

Read this verse, then find a picture (from the back of the book or from a magazine) which shows what he is doing and stick it in here.

"The Lord watches over everyone who obeys him, and he listens to their prayers." 1 Peter 3:12

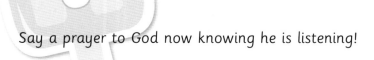

Say a prayer to God now knowing he is listening!

My birthday

Draw or stick in a new and an old picture of yourself. Label the pictures with how old you are in each. Thank God for three good things about being the age you are now.

My friend's birthday

Draw or stick in a picture of your friend. Add birthday pictures like a cake, balloons or streamers. Write three things which you like about them. Thank God for your friend. You could use these ideas to make a card for them!

My brother's/sister's birthday

Draw a picture of you and your brother/sister, and the present you think they would most like to get. Think of a special time you have spent together and thank God for it.

My brother's/sister's birthday

Think of some kind things to say to your brother/sister on their birthday. Write them here and then remember to say them or write them in a card.

My mum's/dad's birthday

Draw or stick in a new and an old picture of your mum or dad. Label the pictures with how old they are in each. Thank God for three good things about them.

My mum's/dad's birthday

Thank God for something kind your mum or dad has done for you. Make a secret plan to do something really kind for them on their birthday. Don't tell them, just write or draw your plan here.

My choice activities

New Year

Write the numbers of the years just finishing and starting. Under them draw or write something great to thank God for from the old year and something you'd like God's help with in the new year.

Mother's Day

Write your mum's name down the side of the page, then write a word which describes her for each letter of her name. Make this into a prayer to God thanking him for your mum!

Father's Day

Think about all the things your dad can do. Write a list or draw pictures of them. Thank God for your amazing dad and all the things he can do!

Easter

Make an Easter garden, like the one Jesus was buried in. As you work, ask a grown-up about what Jesus did. You could use a tray, some stones, sticks and bits of grass. Take a picture and stick it in here.

Easter

Stick in a piece of the wrapping from an Easter egg. Write a prayer thanking God for all your food, and asking him to help children who are hungry.

Easter

Ask someone to read you the Easter story, then draw four pictures to show the main things which happened. Use your pictures to tell someone the story of Easter!

My choice activities

Summer holidays

Draw a picture of you doing your favourite holiday activity. (You might find some ideas in the pictures at the back of the book.) Cut out and stick on a speech bubble from the picture pages and write "Thank you, God!" in it.

Harvest

Write this prayer: "Thank you, God, for..." then stick in the labels or pictures of food you enjoy. When you eat those foods, thank God again!

Christmas

Glue in a Christmas card with a picture of when Jesus was born. Now read the story in Luke 2:1–12. Look at the picture and thank God for Christmas and for sending Jesus to live with his people.

Christmas

Stick in a piece of wrapping paper and think of a present you can give God this Christmas. For example, you could do something kind or helpful. The Bible says that it is better to give than to receive. Test this out and report back here!

Outing

Draw a picture of where you are going on your outing. Ask God to be with you all and keep you safe.

New church

Write a list or draw a picture of the things in your new church which help people talk with God. If there is something about your new church which is a bit confusing, go on a mission to find someone to explain it to you. Then write about it here.

My choice activities

New baby

Carefully draw around the baby's hand. Then draw around your hand. God made both your hands, and he wants both of you to be his friend. Ask God to help you and the baby to be friends with God.

New home

Draw a picture of your favourite room in your new home. Thank God for this room and your new house. Ask God to help you settle in well.

New school

Draw a picture of you at your new school. Talk to God about how you feel about your new school.
Remember he is always with you wherever you go!

New class

Write a list of things you would like in your new class. Then ask God for them.

New term

Draw a picture of your teacher and you then ask God to help them teach you well, and make them patient, fair, kind and wise.

New shoes

Draw round one new shoe on the page, then write the word "peacemaker" inside it. The Bible talks about putting on "shoes of peace" (Ephesians 6:15). Ask God to help you be a peacemaker (someone who helps people get on) wherever you go in your new shoes.

Thank you!

Choose some pictures from the back of the book of things that you would like to thank God for.

You could cut out other pictures too! Stick the pictures on the page and say thank you to God.

Sorry

Choose a picture of something you would like to say sorry to God for. Stick the picture on the page. Draw a big cross through it and say to God, "I know this was wrong, God, and I'm sorry." Remember the Bible says God forgives everyone who's really sorry.

Sorry

Cut out the empty speech bubble from the picture pages and stick it on the page. Write or draw inside the bubble what you need to say sorry to God for. If we are really sorry for what we do wrong, God says, "I forgive you." Hooray!

Help!

Is there something you would like God's help with? Draw a picture of what you would like God to do. As you draw, ask God to help.

Help me do it

Stick a picture here of something good you find difficult to do. Ask God to help you do that thing. Come back to this page later and think about how God has helped you!

You're great!

Think of all your favourite words, like "fantastic", "nice", "good" and "brilliant". Write them down on the page and shout them out to God. Tell him how great he is!

My choice activities

Be with me today

Use this prayer in the morning. Draw pictures of all the things you're going to do today on the page. As you draw, ask God to be with you as you do all these things.

Be with me tonight

Use this prayer when you go to bed. Draw pictures of all the things you have done today. As you work, thank God for being with you. Then ask God to be with you during the night and keep you safe.

Be with me this week

Use this prayer at the beginning of a week. Draw or write some things you will do this week. Say a prayer asking God to be with you everywhere you go.

Be with me this year

On your birthday, at the beginning of a school year or on 1 January, draw and then thank God for your top three things from this year. Then ask God to be with you and guide you in this new year.

Be with me when I'm sick

Draw a picture of yourself being ill. You might like to think of some words which describe how you feel. Tell God all about it, and remember that he is with you, in bed, at the doctor's and even if you have to go to hospital.

Be with me as I leave

If you are leaving somewhere, draw or write here your favourite things about it. Thank God for the good things you'll miss. Imagine something even better than what you are leaving. Thank God that he has lots of new amazing things planned for you!

**From picture
page 1**

**From picture
page 1**

**From picture
page 1**

**From picture
page 1**

**From picture
page 1**

**From picture
page 1**

**From picture
page 2**

**From picture
page 2**

**From picture
page 2**

**From picture
page 2**

**From picture
page 2**

**From picture
page 2**

From picture page 3

From picture page 3

From picture page 3

From picture page 3

From picture page 3

From picture page 3

**From picture
page 4**

**From picture
page 4**

**From picture
page 4**

**From picture
page 4**

**From picture
page 4**

**From picture
page 4**

**From picture
page 5**

**From picture
page 5**

**From picture
page 5**

**From picture
page 5**

**From picture
page 5**

**From picture
page 5**

What next?

Want to read some great Bible stories? Then read these books! Each story has lots of fun pictures to help you enjoy the story and find out more about God.

The Red Book of Must Know Stories
By Alexander Brown
£3.99, 9781844273256

Read the stories of creation, David and Goliath, Daniel and the lions, Jesus' birth and Jesus dying and coming back to life again!

The Green Book of Must Know Stories
By Alexander Brown
£3.99, 9781844273249

Read the stories of Noah, the Ten Commandments, Jesus feeding over 5,000 people, the good Samaritan and the runaway son!

Available from your local Christian bookshop, Scripture Union Mail Order (01908 856006) or online at www.scriptureunion.org.uk/shop.
Prices correct at time of going to press.

What next?

Getting a bit older? Want to pray some more? Why not go on a massive prayer adventure?

Massive Prayer Adventure
By Sarah Mayers
£6.99   978 1 78506 408 1

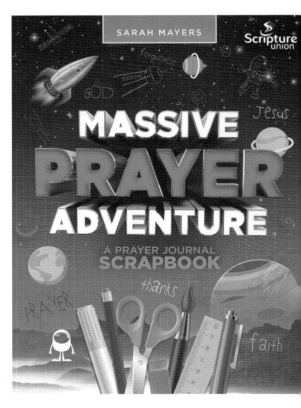

Discover your own personal prayer style with puzzles and quizzes. Try out new places and ideas for meeting God on your own or with your friends. Pray inside and outside, draw, te xt and even fly your prayers to God. And best of all, find out how to hear God speak to you! Are you ready for a prayer adventure?

Available from your local Christian bookshop, Scripture Union Mail Order (01908 856006) or online at www.scriptureunion.org.uk/shop.
Prices correct at time of going to press.